DOUBLE SHOT
OF CLASSIC ROCK

Project Manager: Sy Feldman
Art Design: Jorge Paredes

CONTENTS

ARTIST	SONG	PAGE No.

LONELY PEOPLE

Words and Music by
DAN PEEK and CATHERINE L. PEEK

Don't give up ——— un - til — you drink from the sil -
Don't give up ——— un - til — you drink from the sil -

ver cup ——— and ride that high - way in — the sky. —
ver cup, ——— you nev - er know un - til — you try. —

Well, I'm

on my way, yes, I'm back to

SISTER GOLDEN HAIR

Words and Music by
GERRY BECKLEY

Well, I tried __

Sister Golden Hair - 4 - 1

Sister Golden Hair - 4 - 3

DOCTOR MY EYES

Words and Music by
JACKSON BROWNE

Doctor My Eyes - 6 - 1

2. As I have me.

(Guitar solo-ad lib....

16

FOR A DANCER

Words and Music by
JACKSON BROWNE

Moderately

Keep a fire ___ burn - ing in your eye, ___
Keep a fire ___ for the hu - man race, ___

pay at - ten - tion to the o - pen sky, ___ you nev-er know ___ what
let your prayers go drift - ing in - to space, ___ you nev-er know ___ what

will be com - ing down. ___
will be com - ing down. ___

For a Dancer - 7 - 1

20

do the steps that you've been shown _ by ev-'ry-one you've ev-er known _____

un-til the dance be-comes _ your _ ver-y own. _

No mat-ter how close to yours _ an-oth-er's _ steps have grown, _

in the end _ there _ is _ one _ dance you'll _ do a-lone. _

For a Dancer - 7 - 5

DRIVE

Words and Music by
RIC OCASEK

Who's gon - na tell you when_
Who's gon - na hold you down_

Who's gon - na pick you up___
Who's gon - na pay at - ten - tion

when you_____ fall?_____
to your_____ dreams?_____

Drive - 8 - 4

Drive - 8 - 6

31

Drive - 8 - 8

JUST WHAT I NEEDED

Words and Music by
RIC OCASEK

Medium Rock beat

I don't mind you com-ing here,
I don't mind you hang-ing out

wast-ing all my
and talk-ing in your

time.
sleep.

'Cause when you're stand-ing oh, so___ near,
It does-n't mat-ter where you've__ been

I kind of lose my mind.
as long as it was deep.

It's not the per - fume
You al - ways knew to

that you wear;
wear it well

and

it's not the rib - bons in your hair.
you look so fan - cy. I can tell.

I don't mind you com - ing here
I don't mind you hang - ing out

and wast - ing all my time.
and talk - ing in your sleep.

I guess you're just what I need - ed.

I need - ed

Just What I Needed - 3 - 2

AGAINST ALL ODDS
(Take a Look at Me Now)

Words and Music by
PHIL COLLINS

Slow rock ♩ = 56

1. How can I just let you walk a-way, just let you leave with-out a trace? When I
2.3. (See additional lyrics)

1st & 2nd time mp
3rd time mf

stand here tak-ing ev-'ry breath with you; ooh, you're the

on-ly one who real-ly knew me at all. So take a look at me now,

Against All Odds - 3 - 1

I __ I've got__ to face. Take a good look at me now.__

__I've got__ to take._____

Take a look at me now._____

Verse 2:
How can you just walk away from me,
When all I can do is watch you leave?
'Cause we shared the laughter and the pain,
We even shared the tears.
You're the only one who really knew me at all.
(To Chorus:)

Verse 3:
I wish I could just make you turn around,
Turn around and see me cryin',
There's so much I need to say to you,
So many reasons why.
You're the only one who really knew me at all.
(To Chorus:)

IN THE AIR TONIGHT

Words and Music by
PHIL COLLINS

I can feel it com - ing in the air to-night, ___ oh Lord. ___

And I've been wait-ing for this mo-ment for all my life, ___

oh Lord. ___ Can you feel it com-

Creedence Clearwater Revival

PROUD MARY

Words and Music by
J.C. FOGERTY

Moderately *(with a heavy beat)*

mf

VERSE

Left a good job in the ci-ty, Work-in' for The Man ev-'ry night and day,
Cleaned a lot of plates in Mem-phis, Pumped a lot of pain in New Or-leans,

And I nev-er lost one min-ute of sleep-in', Wor-ry-in' 'bout the way things might have been.
But I nev-er saw the good side of the ci-ty, Un-til I hitched a ride on a riv-er boat queen.

CHORUS

Big wheel keep on turn-in', Proud Mar-y keep on burn-in', Roll-

Proud Mary - 2 - 1

Proud Mary - 2 - 2

TRAVELIN' BAND

Words and Music by
J.C. FOGERTY

Fairly Bright

Sev-en Thir-ty Sev-en com-in' out of the sky.__ Won't you take me down to Mem-phis on a
Take me to the ho - tel,__ Bag-gage gone, oh,__ well.__ Come on,__ come on,__ won't you
Lis-ten to the ra - di-o,__ Talk-in' 'bout the last show.__ Some-one got ex-cit-ed, Had to
Here we come a-gain__ on a Sat-ur-day night__ With your fus-sin' and a-fight-in' Won't you

mid - night ride. I wan - na
get me to my room, I wan - na
call the State Mi-li - tia, wan - na
get me to the rhyme, I wan - na

move.   Play-in' in a Tra-vel-in' Band.__

Yeah!__   Well, I'm fly - in' cross the land.__ try'in'__

48

TEACH YOUR CHILDREN

Words and Music by
GRAHAM NASH

Interlude

Verse 2. Teach Your Children well
Their father's hell
Will slowly go by
And feed them on your dreams
The one they picks
The one you'll know by.

(To Bridge and Interlude)

Verse 3. And you, of the tender years
Can't know the fears
That your elders grew by
And so please help them with your youth
They seek the truth
Before they can die.

Verse 4. Teach your parents well
Their children's hell
Will slowly go by
And feed them on your dreams
The one they picks
The one you'll know by.

(To Bridge and Coda)

Teach Your Children - 3 - 3

CROSBY, STILLS, NASH & YOUNG

WOODSTOCK

Words and Music by
JONI MITCHELL

Slow Folk Style

mp

1. I came up-on a child of God; He was walk-ing a-long the
   can I walk be-side you? I have come here to lose the
   time we got to Wood - stock We were half a mil - lion

road And I asked him, "Where are you go - ing?" This he
smog And I feel to be a cog in some-thing
strong And ev - 'ry - where was song and cel - e -

told me: "I'm
turn - ing. May -
bra - tion. And

Woodstock - 3 - 1

LONG TRAIN RUNNIN'

Words and Music by
TOM JOHNSTON

Long Train Runnin' - 6 - 1

56

58

where would you be now?

Vocal Ad Lib

Got to get it, baby, baby, won't you move it down?
Won't you move it down?
Baby, baby, baby, baby, won't you move it down?
When the big train run
And the train is movin' on
I got to keep on movin',
Keep on movin',
Keep on movin',
Gonna keep on movin'.

DOOBIE BROTHERS

WHAT A FOOL BELIEVES

Words and Music by
MICHAEL McDONALD
and KENNY LOGGINS

Moderately bright, lightly

What a Fool Believes - 6 - 3

Bm7
A/C♯
2 fr.
D
G
E/F♯
And noth - ing at all
is send - ing him some -
E
B/D♯
4 fr.
G♯m7
4 fr.
C♯m7
4 fr.
E/F♯
(Right back there a - lone.)
where back in his long ago
where he can still be -
G♯m7
4 fr.
E/F♯
E
B/D♯
4 fr.
G♯m7
4 fr.
3
lieve there's a place in his life.
Some-how, some - day,
C♯m7
4 fr.
E/F♯
G♯m
4 fr.
Tacet
E/F♯
E
she will re - turn!

DESPERADO

Words and Music by
DON HENLEY and GLENN FREY

Des - per - a - do, why don't_ you come to your sens - es? You been out rid - in' fenc - es for

Desperado - 6 - 1

day. _____ You're los-in' all__ your highs_ and lows.__ Ain't it

fun-ny how__ the feel-in' goes__ a-way?_____

____ Des - per-a - do, why don't_ you

come to your sens-es? Come down from your fenc-es,_____

o - pen the gate.___ It may be rain - in', but there's a

rain - bow a - bove you. ___ You bet - ter let some - bod - y love___ you,

you ___ bet - ter let some - bod - y love ___ you ___ be-

fore it's too ___ late. ___

HOTEL CALIFORNIA

Words and Music by
DON HENLEY, GLENN FREY
and DON FELDER

On a dark des - ert high - way,   cool   wind   in   my
Her mind is Tif - fa - ny twist - ed.   She got the Mer - ce - des

Hotel California - 7 - 1

74

Hotel California - 7 - 2

DON'T STOP

Words and Music by
CHRISTINE McVIE

Medium Rock beat

If you wake up and don't want to smile;___ if it takes just a
Why not think a-bout times___ to come,___ and not a-bout the___
All I want is to see you___ smile,___ if it takes just a

lit - tle while,___ o-pen your eyes and look at the day.___
things that you've done.___ If your___ life was bad to___ you,___
lit - tle while. I know you don't be - lieve that it's true.___

You'll see things in a dif-f'rent___ way._____
just think what to - mor-row will do._____
I nev-er meant an - y harm to____ you._____

Don't stop

YOU MAKE LOVIN' FUN

Words and Music by
CHRISTINE McVIE

You Make Lovin' Fun - 3 - 1

Lyrics:

Oh, _____ can it be so?
You, _____ you make lov-ing fun.

This feel - ing fol - lows me wher - ev - er I go.
And I don't have__ to tell you you're the on - ly__ one.

I nev-er did be - lieve _____ in__ mir - a - cles. _____

But I've a feel-ing it's time to try. _____

You Make Lovin' Fun - 3 - 2

GLENN FREY

SMUGGLER'S BLUES

Words and Music by
GLENN FREY and JACK TEMPCHIN

ba - by here's your tick - et, put the suit - case in your hand, here's
lots of shad - y char - ac - ters lots of dirt - y deals ev -
prop - ping up the gov - ern - ments of Col - um - bi - a and Per - u you ask

— a lit - tle mon - ey now do it just the way we planned You be
'ry name's an al - i - as in case some - bod - y squeals It's the
— an - y D. E. A. man, he'll say there's noth - in' we can do From the

cool for twen - ty hours and I'll pay you twen - ty grand
lure of eas - y mon - ey it's got - ta ver - y strong ap - peal
of - fice of the Pres - i - dent right down to me and you

Smuggler's Blues - 5 - 3

YOU BELONG TO THE CITY

Words and Music by
GLENN FREY and JACK TEMPCHIN

Medium Rock tempo

The sun goes down,— the night rolls in:— you can feel it start-ing all o-ver a-gain.— The moon comes up— and the mu-sic calls:— you're get-tin' tired of star-ing at the same four walls.— You're

You Belong to the City - 5 - 1

you be-long__ to the cit-y, you be-long__ to the night,__

liv-in in a riv-er of dark-ness be-neath the

ne-on lights.__ You were born__ in the cit-y,

con-crete un-der your feet,__ { it's
{ it's

FOLLOW YOU, FOLLOW ME

Words and Music by
TONY BANKS, PHIL COLLINS
and MIKE RUTHERFORD

Stay with me. My love, I hope you'll al-
With the dark I see so ver-y clear-

ways be right here by my side if ev-er I need you,
ly now. All my fears are drift-ing by me so slow-ly now,

Follow You, Follow Me - 3 - 1

Follow You, Follow Me - 3 - 3

IN TOO DEEP

Words and Music by
TONY BANKS, PHIL COLLINS
and MIKE RUTHERFORD

All that time I was search-ing with no-where to run ___ to it

Oh I know you're going but I can't be-lieve ___ it's the

start-ed me ___ think-ing wondering what I _____ could make ___ of my life ___

way that you're_ leav-ing it's like we never knew each oth - er at all ___

SUGAR MAGNOLIA

Words by
ROBERT HUNTER and BOB WEIR

Music by
BOB WEIR

TRUCKIN'

Words by
ROBERT HUNTER

Music by
JERRY GARCIA, BOB WEIR
and PHIL LESH

Truckin' - 10 - 1

114

Ar-rows of ne-on and flash-ing mar-quees out on Main Street,_ Chi-
Most of the cats that you meet on the street speak of true love._

ca-go, New York, De-troit, and it's all on the same street._ Your
Most of the time they're sit-tin' and cry-in' at home.

typ-i-cal cit-y in-volved in a typ-i-cal day-dream,_
One of these days they know they got-ta get go-in'____

hang it up and see what to-mor-row brings._
out of the door and down to the street all a-lone.

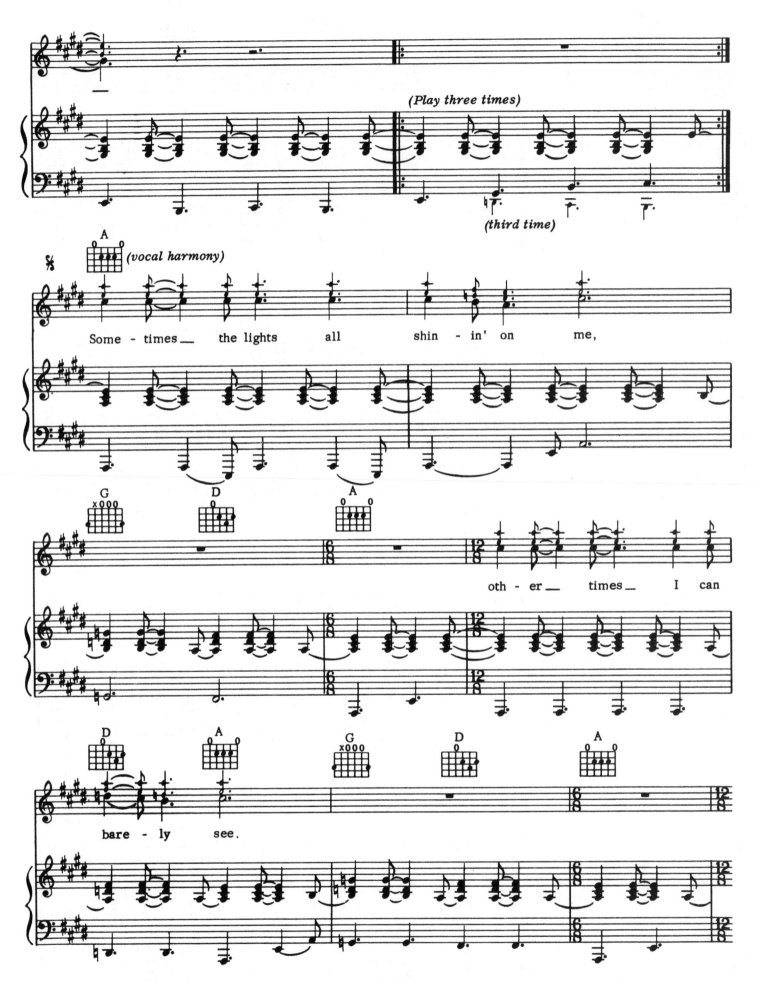

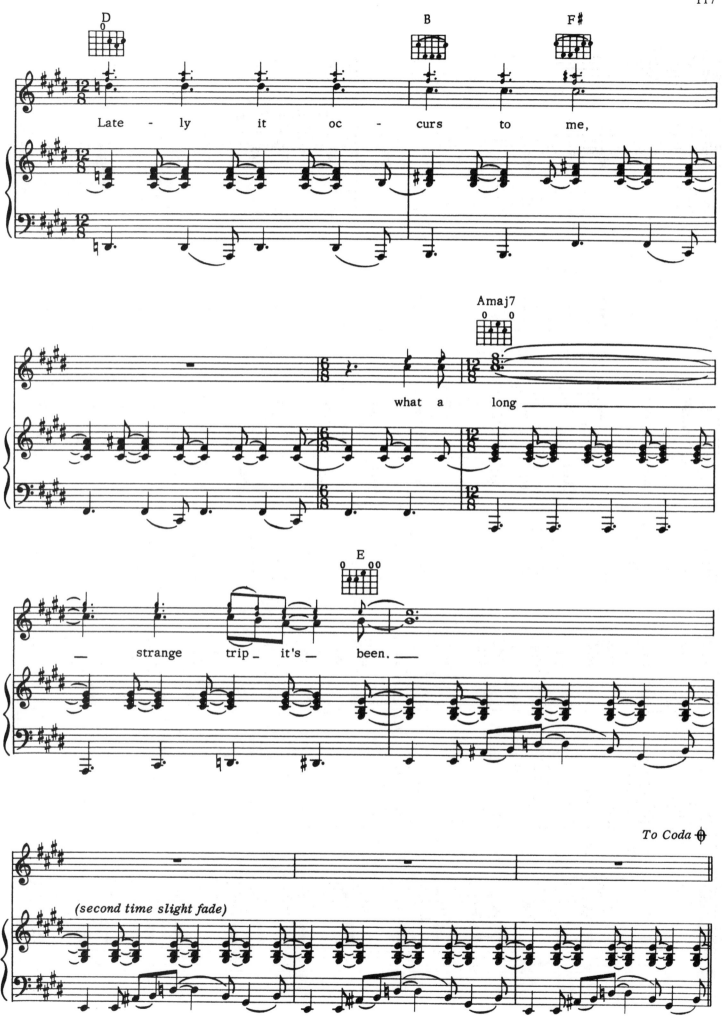

118

Truckin' - 10 - 7

You're sick of hang-in' a-round, and you'd like to trav - el. __ Get

tired __ of trav-el-lin', you want to set-tle down. __ I

guess they can't re-voke __ your soul for try - in', __ get

D. S. 𝄋 al Coda 𝄌

out of the door, light out and look all a - round. __

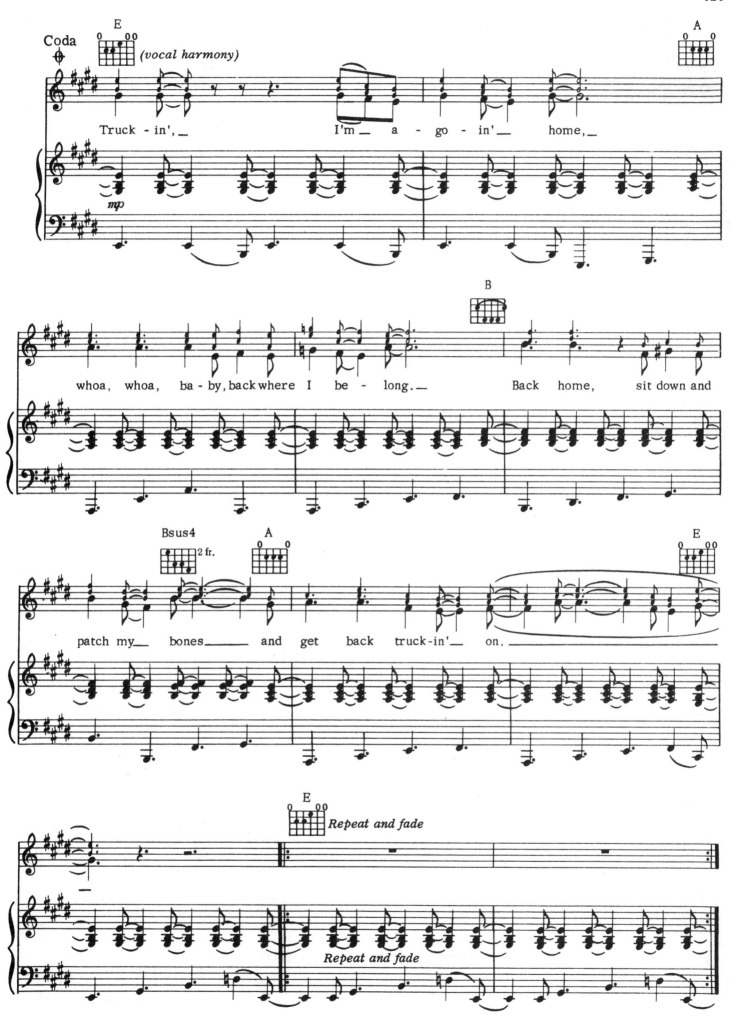

Truck-in', I'm a go-in' home, whoa, whoa, ba-by, back where I be-long. Back home, sit down and patch my bones and get back truck-in' on.

Repeat and fade

BARRACUDA

Words and Music by
ANN WILSON, NANCY WILSON,
ROGER FISHER and MICHAEL DEROSIER

Barracuda - 4 - 1

124

Barracuda - 4 - 3

DOWN ON ME

Words and Music by
ANN WILSON, SUSAN ENNIS
and NANCY WILSON

Please, _____ please, please _____ don't fight me, ba - by!
All, _____ all, all _____ these nights I rocked you.
You _____ know _____ I can't re - sist it.

You know this si - lence has got to stop.
Did - n't I lay it on you e - nough?
I got a need for you.

Down on Me - 4 - 1

I feel___ ro - mance ___ when we move. _____

THE BOYS OF SUMMER

Words and Music by
DON HENLEY and MIKE CAMPBELL

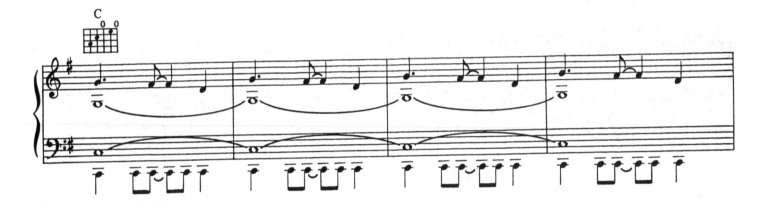

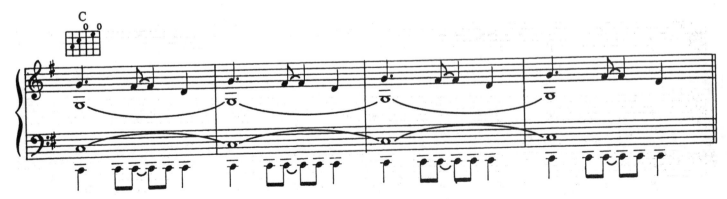

The Boys of Summer - 5 - 2

by your house though I know you're not home.

But I can see you, your brown skin

shin-in' in the sun. You got your hair combed back and your

sun-glass-es on, ba-by. And I can

2. I never will forget those nights. I wonder if it was a dream.
   Remember how you made me crazy? Remember how I made you scream?
   Now I don't understand what happened to our love.
   But babe, I'm gonna get you back. I'm gonna show you what I'm made of.

   I can see you, your brown skin shinin' in the sun.
   I see you walkin' real slow and you're smilin' at everyone.
   I can tell you my love for you will still be strong
   After the boys of summer have gone.

3. Out on the road today I saw a "Deadhead" sticker on a Cadillac.
   A little voice inside my head said, "Don't look back. You can never look back."
   I thought I knew what love was. What did I know?
   Those days are gone forever. I should just let 'em go, but

   I can see you, your brown skin shinin' in the sun.
   You got that top pulled down and that radio on, baby.
   And I can tell you my love for you will still be strong
   After the boys of summer have gone.

   I can see you, your brown skin shinin' in the sun.
   You got that hair slicked back and those Wayfarers on, baby.
   I can tell you my love for you will still be strong
   After the boys of summer have gone.

DON HENLEY

THE HEART OF THE MATTER

Words and Music by
DON HENLEY, MIKE CAMPBELL
and JOHN DAVID SOUTHER

Moderately slow

I got the call to-day, I didn't want to hear but I knew that it would come.
(See additional lyrics)

An old, true friend of ours was talk-in' on the phone, she said you

The Heart of the Matter - 6 - 1

The Heart of the Matter - 6 - 5

and the ash - es will scat - ter. So, I'm think - in' a - bout for - give - ness,
for - give - ness,

for - give - ness e - ven if,___ e - ven if___ you don't love___ me.

Additional Lyrics

Verse 2: These times are so uncertain
There's a yearning undefined
... people filled with rage
We all need a little tenderness
How can love survive in such a graceless age?
The trust and self-assurance that lead to happiness
They're the very things we kill, I guess
Pride and competition
cannot fill these empty arms
And the work I put between us
doesn't keep me warm

Chorus 2: I'm learning to live without you now
But I miss you, baby
The more I know, the less I understand
All the things I thought I'd figured out
I have to learn again
I've been trying to get down
to the heart of the matter
But everything changes
and my friends seem to scatter
But I think it's about forgiveness
Forgiveness
Even if, even if you don't love me anymore.

LYNYRD SKYNYRD

FREE BIRD

Words and Music by
RON VAN ZANT and
ALLEN COLLINS

If I leave here to - mor - row, Would you still re-mem-ber
Bye, bye ba-by it's been a sweet love though this feel-ing I can't

me? For I must be trav-ling on now
change. But please don't take it so bad - ly

142

Free Bird - 3 - 2

SATURDAY NIGHT SPECIAL

Words and Music by
RON VAN ZANT and
ED KING

Saturday Night Special - 3 - 1

146

ADDITIONAL LYRICS

Verse 2.
Big Jim's been drinkin' whiskey
And playin' poker on a losin' night
Pretty soon big Jim starts a-thinkin'
Somebody been cheatin' and lyin'
So big Jim commences to fightin'
I wouldn't tell you no lie.
And big Jim done pulled his pistol
Shot his friend right between the eyes.

Repeat Chorus

Verse 3.
Hand guns are made for killin'
Ain't no good for nothin' else
And if you like to drink your whiskey
You might even shoot yourself
So why don't we dump them people
To the bottom of the sea.
Before some fool come around here
Wanna shoot either you or me.

Saturday Night Special - 3 - 3

JOHN MELLENCAMP

HURTS SO GOOD

Words and Music by
JOHN MELLENCAMP
and GEORGE GREEN

150

JOHN MELLENCAMP

JACK AND DIANE

Words and Music by
JOHN MELLENCAMP

A lit - tle dit - ty   a - bout Jack and Di - ane. _____

Jack and Diane - 8 - 1

two A-mer-i-can kids grow-in' up in the heart - land.

Jack, he's gon-na be_____ a

foot - ball star;_____ Di - ane deb-u-

tante back seat of Jack - y's car.

Jack and Diane - 8 - 2

153

154

155

Jack and Diane - 8 - 4

156

Jack and Diane - 8 - 5

Oh, let it rock, let it roll.

Let the Bi-ble belt come and save my soul.

Hold - in' on to six - teen as long as you can; _____

_____ change is com - in' 'round real soon, make us

D. S. 𝄋 al Coda ⊕

Coda
⊕

wom - en and men.

A little dit - ty a - bout Jack and Di - ane, _____

two A-mer-i-can kids do-in' the

Repeat and fade

best that they___ can.

NIGHTS IN WHITE SATIN

Words and Music by
JUSTIN HAYWARD

YOUR WILDEST DREAMS

Words and Music by
JUSTIN HAYWARD

are, I won-der if_ you think a-bout_ me.

Once up-on_ a time_ in your wild - est

Repeat and fade

dreams._____ In your wild - est

3rd Verse: Once beneath the stars
The universe was ours.
Love was all we knew
And all I knew was you.
I wonder if you know
I wonder if you
Think about it.
Once upon a time
In your wildest dreams.

4th Verse: *Instrumental*

DOMINO

Words and Music by
VAN MORRISON

Don't want to dis-cuss it,
There's no need for arg-u-ment,

I think it's time for a change
there's no arg-u-ment at all.

You may get dis-gust-ed
And if you nev-er hear from him,

and think I'm strange,
that just means he did-n't

call.
Or vice-a ver-sa,

in that case I'll go un-der-ground,

Domino - 3 - 1

Roll me o-ver, Ro-me - o, there you go.— I said:

Oh,_____ oh,_____ Dom - i - no,—

Oh,_____ oh,_____ Dom - i - no.—

ADDITIONAL VERSE

No need to prolong it,
Causes too much needless pain,
And it just don't make any sense
To go through it all again.
No need to overload
Lay everything on someone,
No reason to explode
There's enough in this for everyone.
(Chorus)

MOONDANCE

Words and Music by
VAN MORRISON

DON'T DO ME LIKE THAT

Words and Music by
TOM PETTY

(1) I was talk-in' with a friend of mine, said a wom-an had hurt his pride,__

(Verse 2.3.) See additional lyrics

Don't Do Me Like That - 5 - 1

178

some-where deep, down in-side,___ some-one is say - in'. "Love___

___ does-n't last___ that___ long."___

I've had this feel-in' in-side___ night out and day___ in, and

ba-by I can't take___ it no more.___

D.S. al Coda

Don't Do Me Like That - 5 - 4

Additional Lyrics

Verses 2. & 3.

Listen honey, can you see ? Baby, it would bury me
If you were in the public eye givin' someone else a try.
And you know you better watch your step or you're gonna get hurt yourself.
Someone's gonna tell you lies, cut you down to size.

(To Chorus:)

REFUGEE

Words and Music by
TOM PETTY and MICHAEL CAMPBELL

Moderately (♩ = 120)

Play 4 times

(1) We got some-thin', we both know it, we don't talk too much a-bout ___

Verse 2.,3. - See additional lyrics

___ it. Ain't no real_big se - cret,

all the same, some-how, we get a - round it. Lis-ten,

Refugee - 4 - 1

To Coda

E   F#m   A   E

live like a ref - u - gee._____

A

Ba - by, we ain't the first._ I'm sure a lot of oth - er

D

lov - ers been burned._ Right now this seems real __ to you,__ but it's

E   D.C. al Coda

one of those things you got - ta feel to be true.___

Refugee - 4 - 3

Ba-by, you don't __ have __ to live like a ref-u-gee.

Repeat ad lib & Fade

(instr. solo ad lib)

(Additional Lyrics)

Verse 2:	Somewhere, somehow, somebody must have kicked you around some.
	Tell me why you want to lay there, revel in your abandon.
	Honey,
Chorus 2:	It don't make no difference to me, baby,
	Everybody's had to fight to be free, you see,
	You don't have to live like a refugee. (to 2nd ending)
Verse 3:	Somewhere, somehow, somebody must have kicked you around some.
	Who knows ? Maybe you were kidnapped, tied up, taken away, and held for ransom.
	Honey,
Chorus 3:	It don't really matter to me, baby,
	Everybody's had to fight to be free, you see,
	You don't have to live like a refugee. (to 3rd ending)

THE SPIRIT OF RADIO

Words by
NEIL PEART

Music by
GEDDY LEE and ALEX LIFESON

The Spirit of Radio - 8 - 1

The Spirit of Radio - 8 - 2

186

The Spirit of Radio - 8 - 3

188

mo - tion - al feed - back on a time - less wave - length,

bear - ing a gift __ be - yond price, al - most __

free.

E   B

All this ma - chin - er - y, mak - ing mod - ern mu - sic, can

TOM SAWYER

Words by
PYE DUBOIS and NEIL PEART

Music by
GEDDY LEE and ALEX LIFESON

Tom Sawyer - 6 - 1

194

Tom Sawyer - 6 - 3

space he in - vades,__ he gets by_____ on you.

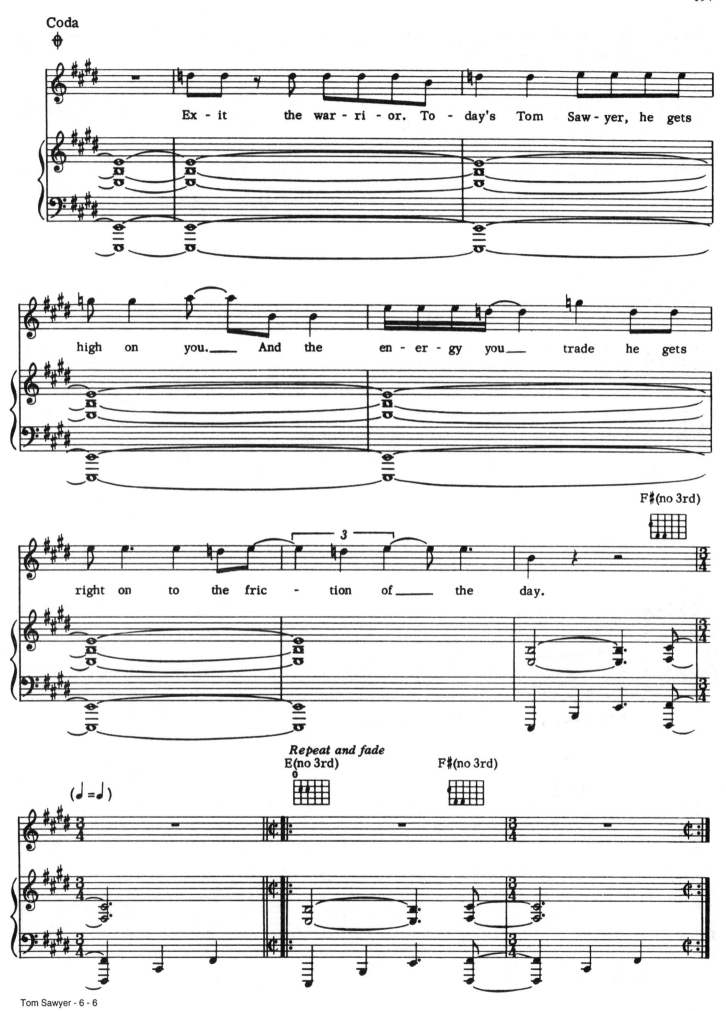

Coda

Ex - it the war - ri - or. To - day's Tom Saw - yer, he gets high on you.___ And the en - er - gy you___ trade he gets right on to the fric - tion of ___ the day.

F#(no 3rd)

Repeat and fade
E(no 3rd)　　F#(no 3rd)

(♩ = ♩)

NIGHT MOVES

Words and Music by
BOB SEGER

Night Moves - 9 - 1

202

night moves, ____ try'n' to lose the awk-ward, teen-age blues, ___

___ work-in' on our night moves.

It was just like south-ern Mich-i-gan sum-mer-time.

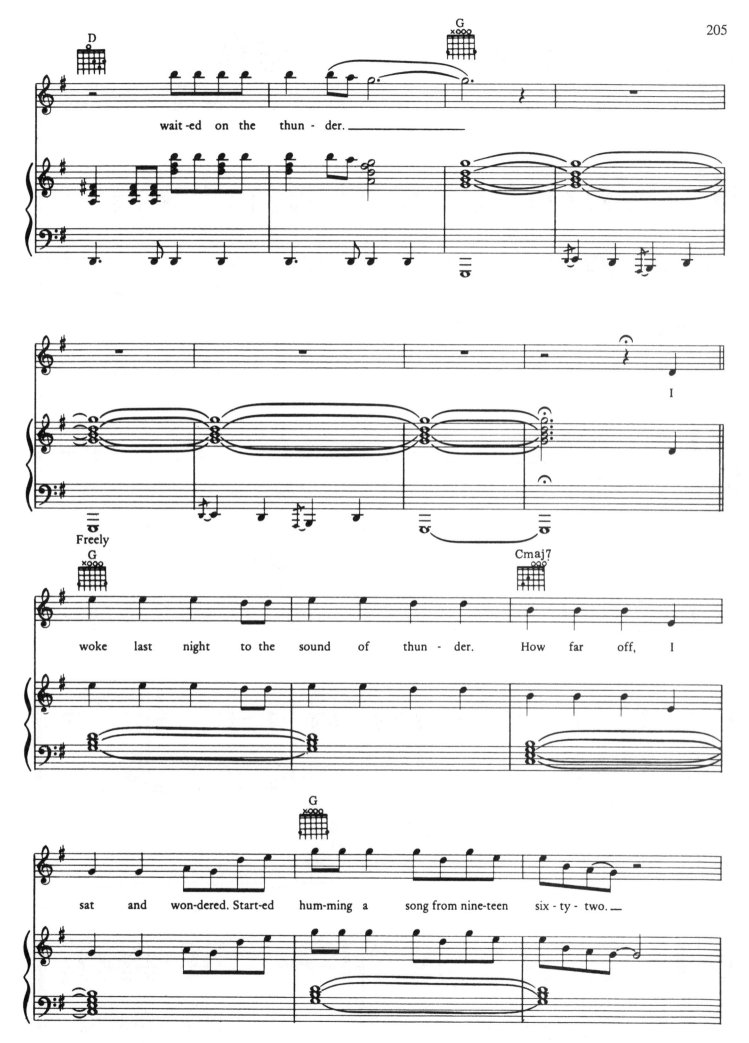

wait-ed on the thun - der. _____

woke last night to the sound of thun - der. How far off, I

sat and won-dered. Start-ed hum-ming a song from nine-teen six-ty-two. __

Freely

BOB SEGER

OLD TIME ROCK & ROLL

Words and Music by
GEORGE JACKSON and
THOMAS EARL JONES III

Rock and Roll Tempo
♩ = 128

Just take those old re-cords off the shelf;___ I sit and lis-ten to them by my-self.___ To-days mu-sic ain't got the same soul,

dis - co, you'll nev - er e - ven get me out on the floor.___ In ten min-utes I'll be late for the door,—

Old Time Rock & Roll - 4 - 1

I like that old___ time a rock and roll.___ Don't try to take me to a
I like that old___ time a rock and roll.___

Still like that old time a rock and roll,___ that kind of mu - sic just
(Chorus)

soothes the soul.___ I rem - i - nisce a - bout the

days of old___ with that old_____ time a

rock and roll.____

Won't go to hear 'em play a   Still like that old____ time a

3. (Won't go to hear 'em play a) tango
I'd rather hear some blues or funky old soul.
There's only one sure way to get me to go
Start playing old time rock and roll.

4. Call me a relic call me what you will
Say I'm old-fashioned say I'm over the hill
Today's music ain't got the same soul
I like that old time rock and roll.

(To Chorus)

BRUCE SPRINGSTEEN

DANCING IN THE DARK

Words and Music by
BRUCE SPRINGSTEEN

Verse 2:
Message keeps getting clearer;
Radio's on and I'm moving 'round the place.
I check my look in the mirror;
I wanna change my clothes, my hair, my face.
Man, I ain't getting nowhere just living in a dump like this.
There's something happening somewhere;
Baby I just know there is.
(To Chorus:)

Verse 3:
Stay on the streets of this town
And they'll be carving you up all right.
They say you got to stay hungry;
Hey baby I'm just about starving tonight.
I'm dying for some action;
I'm sick of sitting 'round here trying to write this book.
I need a love reaction;
Come on now baby gimme just one look.
(To Chorus:)

FIRE

Words and Music by
BRUCE SPRINGSTEEN

Fire - 3 - 1

Fire - 3 - 3

STEPHEN STILLS

CARRY ON

Words and Music by
STEPHEN STILLS

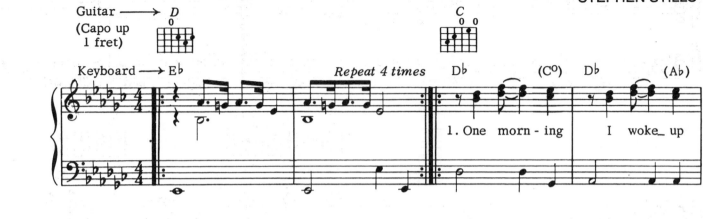

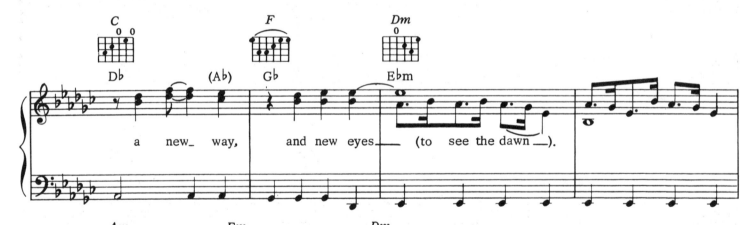

Carry On - 3 - 1

Last time repeat last 4 measures and fade.

D. S.

ADDITIONAL VERSES

2. The sky is clearing and the night has cried enough
   The sun he comes, the world to soften up
   Rejoice, rejoice, we have no choice but to carry on.

3. The fortunes of fables are able to see the stars,
   Now witness the quickness with which we carry on
   To sing the blues, you've got to live the dues and Carry On.

   Girl, when I was on my own
   Chasing you down
   What was it made you run
   Tryin' your best just to get around
   The questions of a thousand dreams
   What you do and what you see
   Lover, can you talk to me?

STEPHEN STILLS

LOVE THE ONE YOU'RE WITH

Words and Music by
STEPHEN STILLS

Love the One You're With - 3 - 1

LOCOMOTIVE BREATH

Words and Music by
IAN ANDERSON

Locomotive Breath - 2 - 1

Locomotive Breath - 2 - 2

JETHRO TULL

LIVING IN THE PAST

Words and Music by
IAN ANDERSON

Hap - py___ and I'm
Once I___ used to

smil - ing,___ walk a mile to___ drink your wa - ter.___ You
join in___ ev - 'ry boy and___ girl was my friend.___

AFRICA

Words and Music by
DAVID PAICH and JEFF PORCARO

He turned_ to me_ as if_ to say,_
I seem_ to cure_ what's deep_ in - side,_

"Hur - ry, boy,_ it's wait - ing there_ for you."_
fright - ened of_ this thing that I've_ be - come._

It's gon - na take a lot_

_ to drag_ me a - way_ from you._

Africa - 6 - 4

Repeat and fade

Africa - 6 - 6

ROSANNA

Words and Music by
DAVID PAICH

All I wan - na do when I wake up in the morn - ing is
I can see your face still shin - ing through the win - dow on the

see your eyes, _____ Ro - san - na, __ Ro - san - na. __
oth - er side, _____ Ro - san - na, __ Ro - san - na.

Rosanna - 5 - 1

have to say:___

Meet you all the way,

meet you all the way,

Ro - san - na,_____ yeah.___ Meet you

Rosanna - 5 - 4

240

all the way,   meet you

all the way,   Ro - san - na, _____ yeah. __

Repeat and fade

Van Halen

JUMP

Words and Music by
EDWARD VAN HALEN, ALEX VAN HALEN,
MICHAEL ANTHONY and DAVID LEE ROTH

Jump - 8 - 1

243

Jump - 8 - 3

Jump - 8 - 5

246

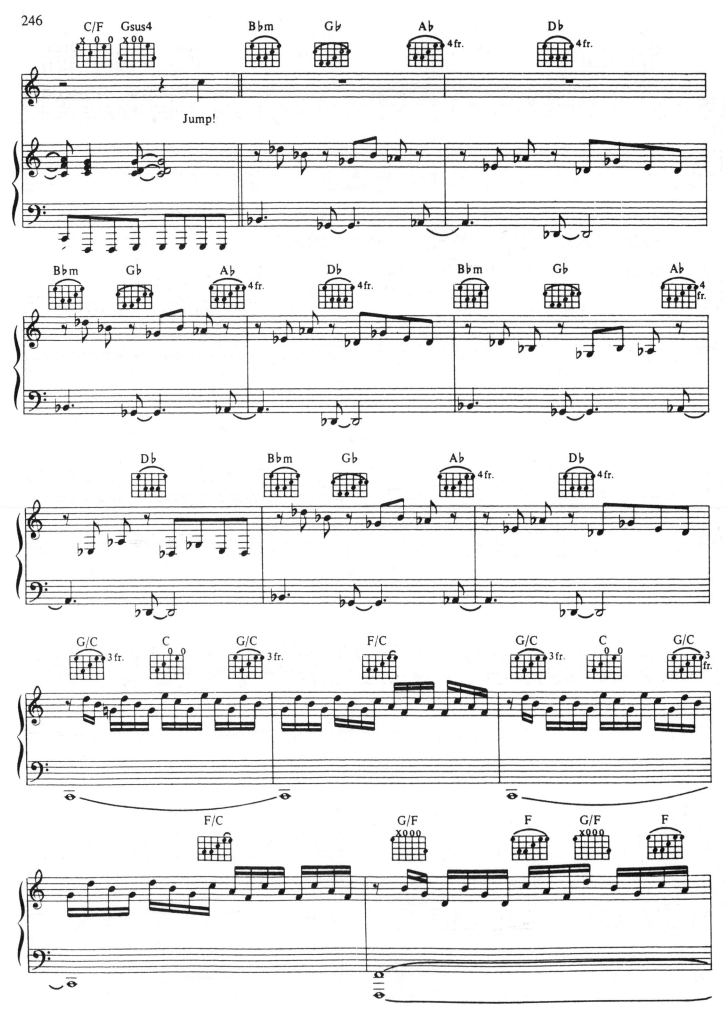

Jump!

Jump - 8 - 6

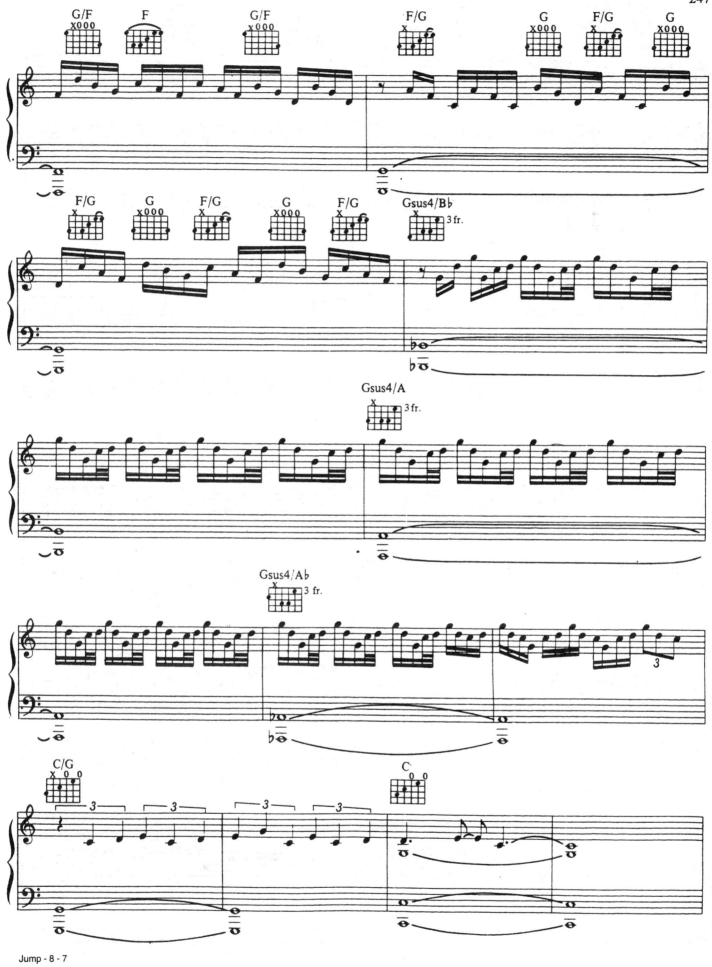

248

VAN HALEN

PANAMA

Words and Music by
EDWARD VAN HALEN, ALEX VAN HALEN,
MICHAEL ANTHONY and DAVID LEE ROTH

Bright Rock beat

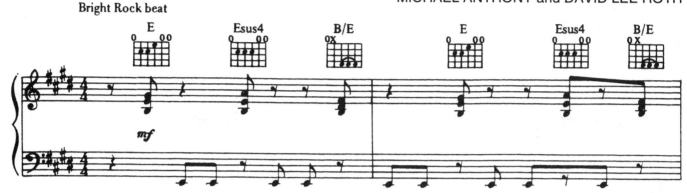

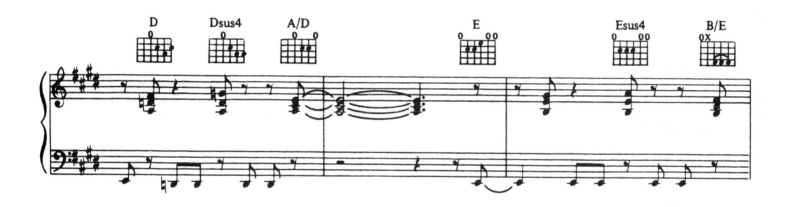

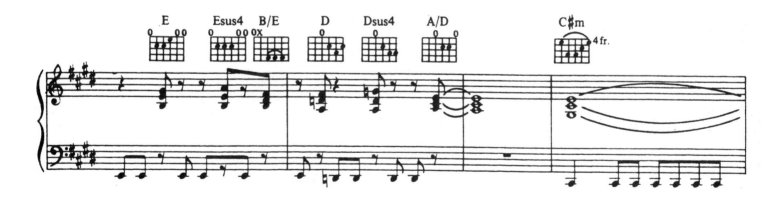

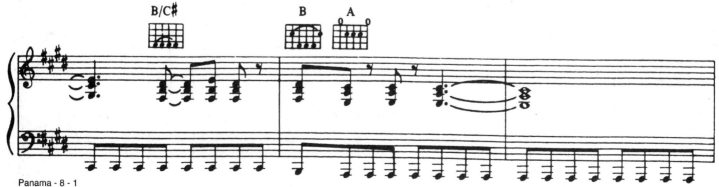

Panama - 8 - 1

Jump   back.
Ain't noth - in' like it,   her

254

Panama - 8 - 6

HIGHER LOVE

Words and Music by
STEVE WINWOOD and WILL JENNINGS

Think a-bout____ it, there must be____ high-er love,
-ing and we're just____ hang-ing on,

down in the heart or hid-den in the stars a-bove.____ With-out____ it, life is
fac-ing our fear and stand-ing out there a-lone.____ A yearn-ing, and it's

wast-ed time. Look in-side your heart, I'll look in-side mine.
real to me. There must be some-one who's feel-ing for me.

Higher Love - 5 - 1

ROLL WITH IT

Words and Music by
STEVE WINWOOD, WILL JENNINGS,
EDDIE HOLLAND, LAMONT DOZIER
and BRIAN HOLLAND

Medium Funk

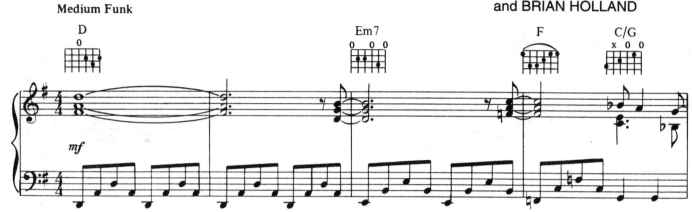

When life

— is too much,— roll with it, ba — by.
way that you love— is good as mon — ey.
-'ll be a day, you'll get there, ba — by.

Don't
I
You'll

Roll With It - 4 - 1

stop and lose your touch,— oh no, ba - by. Hard time knock-
swear by stars a - bove,— sweet as hon - ey. Peo - ple think—
hear the mus - ic play,— you'll dance, ba - by. You'll— leave—

ing— at your door,— I'll tell them you ain't there no more.—
— you're down and out,— You show them what it's all a - bout.—
— bad— times be - hind,— noth - ing but good times on your mind.—

Get on through it, roll with it, ba - by.
You can make it, roll with it, ba - by.
You can do it, roll with it, ba - by.

Roll With It - 4 - 2

Roll With It - 4 - 4

ALL GOOD PEOPLE

Words and Music by
CHRIS SQUIRE

Moderately bright shuffle

I've seen all good peo-ple turn their heads each day so sat-is-fied I'm on my way.

I've seen all good peo-ple turn their heads each day so sat-

All Good People - 3 - 2

268

All Good People - 3 - 3

YES

ROUNDABOUT

Words and Music by
JON ANDERSON and STEVE HOWE

Roundabout - 6 - 1

270

Roundabout - 6 - 2

NEIL YOUNG

AFTER THE GOLD RUSH

Words and Music by
NEIL YOUNG

Well, I

dreamed I saw the knights in ar - mor com - ing, say-in' some-thing a - bout___ a queen..
ly - in' in a burned out base - ment with the full moon in my eyes.___

There were peas-ants sing - in' and drum-mers drum - min' and the
I was hop - in' for___ re - place - ment when the

arch - er split the tree.___ There was a fan - fare blow - in'
sun burst through the sky.___ There was a band___ play - in'

After the Gold Rush - 4 - 1

After the Gold Rush - 4 - 3

NEIL YOUNG

ONLY LOVE CAN BREAK YOUR HEART

Words and Music by
NEIL YOUNG

Only Love Can Break Your Heart - 3 - 3

LEGS

Words and Music by
BILLY GIBBONS, DUSTY HILL
and FRANK BEARD

Legs - 4 - 1

Verse 2: She's got hair down to her fanny
     She's kinda jet set, try undo her panties
     Everytime she's dancin' she knows what to do
     Everybody wants to see, to see if she can use it
     She's so fine, she's all mine
     Girl you got it right.

Instr.: Gtr Solo: //: C#m / F#m :// B / E

Verse 3: She's got legs, she knows how to use them
     She never begs, she knows how to choose them
     She's got a dime all of the time
     Stays out at night, movin' through time
     I'm Oh, I want her, sure I got to have her
     The girl is alright, she's alright.

Instr.: Gtr Solo //: C#m / E ://

Legs - 4 - 4

ZZ TOP

TUSH

Words and Music by
BILLY GIBBONS, DUSTY HILL
and FRANK BEARD

Tush - 2 - 1

INDEX OF SONGS